Eleven Plus
Secondary School Selection

Verbal Reasoning

11+
Daily Practice Tests

20 Tests
Dual Format

Book 1

Introduction

This book is designed to complement the IPS set of verbal reasoning practice papers. It contains short daily practice papers, and uses questions of all of the types covered in the IPS range.

These tests are meant for those who have had some experience of verbal reasoning and the types of questions used.

When practising for tests such as the 11+, or other school entrance exams, most people do not use full length practice papers on a daily basis. However, a few minutes of practice every day can be very beneficial, and it does not put too much strain on the pupil who will sit the exam — which is very important indeed.

I would suggest using these papers in between attempting longer practice papers.

Each test should be completed in between five and six minutes. All the question types used in the IPS range of publications are used in this book.

Good luck.

11+ Team. 2004.

Keep a record of your scores.

Paper	Score:	Paper	Score:
1		11	
2		12	
3		13	
4		14	
5		15	
6		16	
7		17	
8		18	
9		19	
10		20	

Daily Test 1

Question 1

In the question below, the three words in the second group should go together in the same way as the three in the first group. Find the missing word from the second group and write it in the space provide or mark the appropriate box on the multiple choice answer sheet.

radio   [drive]   river

hotel [_____] fired

Question 2

In this question you need to find the number that should appear in the brackets and completes the sum correctly. Write this number in the space provided or mark the appropriate box on the multiple choice answer sheet.

$63 \div 9 \times 3 = 101 - 48 - (\_\_\_\_)$

Question 3

In this question the numbers in each group are related in the same way. You must find the missing number in the third group and write it in the space provided or mark the appropriate box on the multiple choice answer sheet.

(121 [91] 30)   (107 [66] 41)

(115 [____] 37)

Question 4

In the sentence below, one word, which is in capitals, has had **three consecutive** letters taken out. These **three** letters will make one correctly spelt word without changing their order. Write the **three-letter** word in the space provided or mark the appropriate box on the multiple choice answer sheet.

We **LNED** all about the solar system yesterday.

(_____)

Question 5

Below you will see four words and three of their codes. One of the codes is missing. Using the same code, convert the word or number below. Write the answer in the brackets or mark the appropriate box on the multiple choice answer sheet.

ROPE   POUR   POLE   PLAN

3791   3956   2731

Find the code for the word **PANEL** (_____)

Question 6

In the question below, **one** letter from the word on the left must be moved into the word on the right to make **two** new words. The letters must not be re-arranged. **Both** new words must make sense. Write the correct letter in the space provided or mark the appropriate box on the multiple choice answer sheet.

CHEAP   SPIT   (_____)

Question 7

In this question you must find two words, **one** from each group, that are the **closest in meaning**. **Underline** each of these two words or mark the appropriate boxes on the multiple choice answer sheet

(swing swerve jump)

(trade dodge slide)

Question 8

In this question find the two words, one from each group that will complete the sentence in the best way. **Underline** one word from each group or mark the appropriate boxes on the multiple choice answer sheet.

Six is to (hexagon, twelve, three)

as seven is to (days, octagon, fourteen).

Question 9

In each question below, letters stand for numbers. Work out the answer to the sum and write its **letter** in the brackets or mark the appropriate box on the multiple choice answer sheet.

A = 9, B = 18, C = 17, D = 3, E = 12,

$B \div D + A + D = (\_\_\_)$

Question 10

A B C D E F G H I J K L M N O P Q R S T U V W X Y Z

In this question a word had been written in code. An example has been worked out for you. You must now work out the missing word using the same code. Write the word in the space provided or mark the appropriate box on the multiple choice answer sheet.

If the code for **JELLY** is **KDMKZ**

what does **QHUBI** mean? _____

Daily Test 2

Question 1

In the question below, find one letter that will complete the word in front of the brackets and begin the word after the brackets.
The same letter must fit into both sets of brackets.
Write the letter on the answer sheet or mark the appropriate box on the multiple choice answer sheet.

SLI (___) AKE   :   FIL (___) OUNT

Question 2

In this question you need to find the number that should appear in the brackets and will continue the series in the most sensible way. Write this number in the space provided or mark the appropriate box on the multiple choice answer sheet.

7,   5,   6,   4,   5,   3,   (____)

Question 3

In the sentence below, a word of four letters is hidden at the end of one word and the beginning of the next word.
Underline the **pair** of words that contain the hidden word or mark the appropriate box on the multiple choice answer sheet.

Their late arrival spoiled their holiday.

Question 4

A B C D E F G H I J K L M N O P Q R S T U V W X Y Z

In the question below, find the pair of letters that will complete the sentence in the best way and write the correct answer in the answer box or mark the appropriate box on the multiple choice answer sheet.

HM is to **KQ**

as **EH** is to (_____)

Question 5

In the question below, there are two pairs of words. You must find the word from the list that will go equally well with both pairs of words in the brackets.
Underline this word or mark the appropriate box on the multiple choice answer sheet.

SKINNY   SHARP   SLICE   HACK   TRIM

(SLIM   SLENDER)   (CUT   CLIP)

Question 6

In this question there are three pairs of words. You must complete the third pair in the same way as the first two pairs. Write the correct letter in the space provided or mark the appropriate box on the multiple choice answer sheet.

(spill, lips)   (stunt, nuts)

(lived, _____)

Question 7

In the question below, find two words, **one** from each group, that are the **most opposite in meaning**.
Underline each of these two words or mark the appropriate boxes on the multiple choice answer sheet

(extract   taper   seize)

(ventilate   record   release)

Question 8

In the question below, find the **two** words that are **different** from the other three and **underline** them on the answer sheet or mark the appropriate box on the multiple choice answer sheet.

play   frolic   sit   cry   romp

Question 9

A B C D E F G H I J K L M N O P Q R S T U V W X Y Z

In this question you need to find the pair of letters that will complete the sequence in the best way and write the correct answer in the answer box or mark the appropriate box on the multiple choice answer sheet.

DG,   FI,   EH,   GJ,   FI,   (_____)

Question 10

In the question below, choose **two** words, **one** from each set, that will together make **one** correctly spelt word. You may not change the order of the letters.
The word from the set on the top always comes first.
Underline the two words or mark the appropriate boxes on the multiple choice answer sheet.

(go   leave   scram)

(bleed   bled   cut)

Daily Test 3

Question 1

In the question below, the three words in the second group should go together in the same way as the three in the first group. Find the missing word from the second group and write it in the space provide or mark the appropriate box on the multiple choice answer sheet.

bland   [blast]   steal

coach [_____] stale

Question 2

In this question you need to find the number that should appear in the brackets and completes the sum correctly. Write this number in the space provided or mark the appropriate box on the multiple choice answer sheet.

17 + 18 + 19 = 2 x 3 x (_____)

Question 3

In this question the numbers in each group are related in the same way. You must find the missing number in the third group and write it in the space provided or mark the appropriate box on the multiple choice answer sheet.

(24 [2] 6)   (35 [3] 7)

(48 [___] 6)

Question 4

In the sentence below, one word, which is in capitals, has had **three consecutive** letters taken out. These **three** letters will make one correctly spelt word without changing their order. Write the **three-letter** word in the space provided or mark the appropriate box on the multiple choice answer sheet.

Don't drop the plate or it will **STER**.

Answer _____

Question 5

Below you will see four words and three of their codes. One of the codes is missing. Using the same code, convert the word or number below. Write the answer in the brackets or mark the appropriate box on the multiple choice answer sheet.

MAST   SLAM   TALK   LEAK

5826   7219   9256

Find the code for the word **STEAM** (_____)

Question 6

In the question below, **one** letter from the word on the left must be moved into the word on the right to make **two** new words. The letters must not be re-arranged. **Both** new words must make sense.
Write the correct letter in the space provided or mark the appropriate box on the multiple choice answer sheet.

FRAIL   ACTOR   (_____)

Question 7

In this question you must find two words, **one** from each group, that are the **closest in meaning**.
Underline each of these two words or mark the appropriate boxes on the multiple choice answer sheet

(amiable   feasible   durable)

(friendly   cowardly   tiresome)

Question 8

In this question find the two words, one from each group that will complete the sentence in the best way. **Underline** one word from each group or mark the appropriate boxes on the multiple choice answer sheet.

Bicycle is to (saddle, wheel, pedal)

as pram is to (baby, push, stroll).

Question 9

In each question below, letters stand for numbers. Work out the answer to the sum and write its **letter** in the brackets or mark the appropriate box on the multiple choice answer sheet.

A = 4, B = 8, C = 16, D = 2, E = 12,

B x A - B - E = (____)

Question 10

A B C D E F G H I J K L M N O P Q R S T U V W X Y Z

In this question a word had been written in code. An example has been worked out for you. You must now work out the missing word using the same code. Write the word in the space provided or mark the appropriate box on the multiple choice answer sheet.

If the code for **CLEVER** is **FHHRHN**,

what does **SWLJWO** mean? _____

Daily Test 4

Question 1

In the question below, find one letter that will complete the word in front of the brackets and begin the word after the brackets.
The same letter must fit into both sets of brackets.
Write the letter on the answer sheet or mark the appropriate box on the multiple choice answer sheet.

SCAL (___) OST   :   FLA (___) INT

Question 2

In this question you need to find the number that should appear in the brackets and will continue the series in the most sensible way. Write this number in the space provided or mark the appropriate box on the multiple choice answer sheet.

3,   5,   9,   17,   33,   (____)

Question 3

In the sentence below, a word of four letters is hidden at the end of one word and the beginning of the next word.
Underline the **pair** of words that contain the hidden word or mark the appropriate box on the multiple choice answer sheet.

The squeaky door needs oiling immediately.

Question 4

A B C D E F G H I J K L M N O P Q R S T U V W X Y Z

In the question below, find the pair of letters that will complete the sentence in the best way and write the correct answer in the answer box or mark the appropriate box on the multiple choice answer sheet.

BW is to **EU**
as **WB** is to (_____)

Question 5

In the question below, there are two pairs of words. You must find the word from the list that will go equally well with both pairs of words in the brackets.
Underline this word or mark the appropriate box on the multiple choice answer sheet.

TIME   SNIP   POP   BREAK   PAUSE

(CRACK   SNAP)   (INTERVAL   INTERLUDE)

Question 6

In this question there are three pairs of words. You must complete the third pair in the same way as the first two pairs. Write the correct letter in the space provided or mark the appropriate box on the multiple choice answer sheet.

(tender, dent)   (spread, ears)

(barked, _____)

Question 7

In the question below, find two words, **one** from each group, that are the **most opposite in meaning**.
Underline each of these two words or mark the appropriate boxes on the multiple choice answer sheet

(legal   lethal   lethargic)
(kind   harmless   generous)

Question 8

In the question below, find the **two** words that are **different** from the other three and **underline** them on the answer sheet or mark the appropriate box on the multiple choice answer sheet.

crisps   snack   sandwich   banquet   meal

Question 9

A B C D E F G H I J K L M N O P Q R S T U V W X Y Z

In this question you need to find the pair of letters that will complete the sequence in the best way and write the correct answer in the answer box or mark the appropriate box on the multiple choice answer sheet.

DH,   IE,   NB,   SY,   XV,   (_____)

Question 10

In the question below, choose **two** words, **one** from each set, that will together make **one** correctly spelt word. You may not change the order of the letters.
The word from the set on the top always comes first.
Underline the two words or mark the appropriate boxes on the multiple choice answer sheet.

(face   neck   head)
(thirds   bases   quarters)

Daily Test 5

Question 1

In this question there are three pairs of words. You must complete the third pair in the same way as the first two pairs. Write the correct letter in the space provided or mark the appropriate box on the multiple choice answer sheet.

(mumble, mule)   (remain, rein)

(tinder, _____)

Question 2

In the question below, find two words, **one** from each group, that are the **most opposite in meaning**.
Underline each of these two words or mark the appropriate boxes on the multiple choice answer sheet

(copied   alike   print)

(same   dissimilar   paint)

Question 3

In the question below, find the **two** words that are **different** from the other three and **underline** them on the answer sheet or mark the appropriate box on the multiple choice answer sheet.

saxophone   trumpet   violin   trombone   piano

Question 4

A B C D E F G H I J K L M N O P Q R S T U V W X Y Z

In this question you need to find the pair of letters that will complete the sequence in the best way and write the correct answer in the answer box or mark the appropriate box on the multiple choice answer sheet.

FK,   HN,   JQ,   LT,   NW,   (_____)

Question 5

In the question below, choose **two** words, **one** from each set, that will together make **one** correctly spelt word. You may not change the order of the letters.
The word from the set on the top always comes first.
Underline the two words or mark the appropriate boxes on the multiple choice answer sheet.

(pull   carry   transit)

(ore   ion   van)

Question 6

In the question below, find one letter that will complete the word in front of the brackets and begin the word after the brackets.
The same letter must fit into both sets of brackets.
Write the letter between the brackets on the sheet or mark the appropriate box on the multiple choice answer sheet.

GRI (___) AWN   :   TRIE (___) ART

Question 7

In this question you need to find the number that should appear in the brackets and will continue the series in the most sensible way. Write this number in the space provided or mark the appropriate box on the multiple choice answer sheet.

25,   26,   28,   27,   31,   28,   (____)

Question 8

In the sentence below, a word of four letters is hidden at the end of one word and the beginning of the next word. **Underline** the **pair** of words that contain the hidden word or mark the appropriate box on the multiple choice answer sheet.

Olivia sprained her right ankle badly.

Question 9

A B C D E F G H I J K L M N O P Q R S T U V W X Y Z

In the question below, find the pair of letters that will complete the sentence in the best way and write the correct answer in the answer box or mark the appropriate box on the multiple choice answer sheet.

CD is to BA

as PC is to (_____)

Question 10

In the question below, there are two pairs of words. You must find the word from the list that will go equally well with both pairs of words in the brackets.
Underline this word or mark the appropriate box on the multiple choice answer sheet.

SUM   COUNT   TOT   LORD   TALLY

(EARL   NOBLEMAN)   (ADD   TOTAL)

Daily Test 6

Question 1

In the question below, **one** letter from the word on the left must be moved into the word on the right to make **two** new words. The letters must not be re-arranged. **Both** new words must make sense.
Write the correct letter in the space provided or mark the appropriate box on the multiple choice answer sheet.

BRAND   CEASED   (_____)

Question 2

In this question you must find two words, **one** from each group, that are the **closest in meaning**.
Underline each of these two words or mark the appropriate boxes on the multiple choice answer sheet

(consent   letter   stamp)

(vowel   envelope   tread)

Question 3

In this question find the two words, one from each group that will complete the sentence in the best way. **Underline** one word from each group or mark the appropriate boxes on the multiple choice answer sheet.

Noisy is to (nosey, quiet, loud)

as silent is to (sound, hushed, night).

Question 4

In each question below, letters stand for numbers. Work out the answer to the sum and write its **letter** in the brackets or mark the appropriate box on the multiple choice answer sheet.

A = 50, B = 100, C = 20, D = 150, E = 10,

E x C - D + A = (____)

Question 5

A B C D E F G H I J K L M N O P Q R S T U V W X Y Z

In this question a word had been written in code. An example has been worked out for you. You must now work out the missing code in the same way. Write the code in the space provided or mark the appropriate box on the multiple choice answer sheet.

If the code for **LEASE** is **NDCRG**,

what is the code for **SWOOP**?

_____

Question 6

In the question below, the three words in the second group should go together in the same way as the three in the first group. Find the missing word from the second group and write it in the space provide or mark the appropriate box on the multiple choice answer sheet.

sheet   [teach]   chant

alert (_____) abide

Question 7

In this question you need to find the number that should appear in the brackets and completes the sum correctly. Write this number in the space provided or mark the appropriate box on the multiple choice answer sheet.

24 + 27 + 26 = 42 ÷ 6 x (_____)

Question 8

In this question the numbers in each group are related in the same way. You must find the missing number in the third group and write it in the space provided or mark the appropriate box on the multiple choice answer sheet.

(17 [21] 25)   (15 [24] 33)

(12 [____] 46)

Question 9

In the sentence below, one word, which is in capitals, has had **three consecutive** letters taken out. These **three** letters will make one correctly spelt word without changing their order. Write the **three-letter** word in the space provided or mark the appropriate box on the multiple choice answer sheet.

John was told to **SD** in the corner.

Answer _____

Question 10

Below you will see four words and three of their codes. One of the codes is missing. Using the same code, convert the word or number below. Write the answer in the brackets or mark the appropriate box on the multiple choice answer sheet.

NEWT   BOND   TOWN   CONE
3259   1256   5984

Find the word for the code **321891** (_____)

Daily Test 7

Score. _____

Question 1

In the question below, find one letter that will complete the word in front of the brackets and begin the word after the brackets.
The same letter must fit into both sets of brackets.
Write the letter on the answer sheet or mark the appropriate box on the multiple choice answer sheet.

STE (___) ENT   :   FLE (___) ATCH

Question 2

In this question you need to find the number that should appear in the brackets and will continue the series in the most sensible way. Write this number in the space provided or mark the appropriate box on the multiple choice answer sheet.

1,   5,   6,   11,   17,   28,   (____)

Question 3

In the sentence below, a word of four letters is hidden at the end of one word and the beginning of the next word.
Underline the **pair** of words that contain the hidden word or mark the appropriate box on the multiple choice answer sheet.

The fish soup made grandpa ill

Question 4

A B C D E F G H I J K L M N O P Q R S T U V W X Y Z

In the question below, find the pair of letters that will complete the sentence in the best way and write the correct answer in the answer box or mark the appropriate box on the multiple choice answer sheet.

RU is to NW

as QQ is to (_____)

Question 5

In the question below, there are two pairs of words. You must find the word from the list that will go equally well with both pairs of words in the brackets.
Underline this word or mark the appropriate box on the multiple choice answer sheet.

TRUE   SANDY   FAIR   EVEN   TRUST

(BLONDE   LIGHT) (IMPARTIAL   UNBIASED)

Question 6

In this question there are three pairs of words. You must complete the third pair in the same way as the first two pairs. Write the correct letter in the space provided or mark the appropriate box on the multiple choice answer sheet.

(atlases, last)   (adheres, hard)

(ascends, _____)

Question 7

In the question below, find two words, **one** from each group, that are the **most opposite in meaning**.
Underline each of these two words or mark the appropriate boxes on the multiple choice answer sheet

(rode   rude   unlawful)

(illegal   funny   courteous)

Question 8

In the question below, find the **two** words that are **different** from the other three and **underline** them on the answer sheet or mark the appropriate box on the multiple choice answer sheet.

mystery   puzzle   haunted   ghostly   riddle

Question 9

A B C D E F G H I J K L M N O P Q R S T U V W X Y Z

In this question you need to find the pair of letters that will complete the sequence in the best way and write the correct answer in the answer box or mark the appropriate box on the multiple choice answer sheet.

KL,   EM,   ZO,   VR,   SV,   (_____)

Question 10

In the question below, choose **two** words, **one** from each set, that will together make **one** correctly spelt word. You may not change the order of the letters.
The word from the set on the top always comes first.
Underline the two words or mark the appropriate boxes on the multiple choice answer sheet.

(blew   blue   blow)

(bell   ball   belt)

Daily Test 8

Question 1

In the question below, **one** letter from the word on the left must be moved into the word on the right to make **two** new words. The letters must not be re-arranged. **Both** new words must make sense.
Write the correct letter in the space provided or mark the appropriate box on the multiple choice answer sheet.

GRIPE   HOST   (_____)

Question 2

In this question you must find two words, **one** from each group, that are the **closest in meaning**.
Underline each of these two words or mark the appropriate boxes on the multiple choice answer sheet

(amble   gamble   tangle)

(wonder   wander   bramble)

Question 3

In this question find the <u>two</u> words, <u>one</u> from each group that will complete the sentence in the best way.
Underline one word from each group or mark the appropriate boxes on the multiple choice answer sheet.

Grown is to (enlarged, raised, groan)

as blew is to (blown, blue, wind).

Question 4

In each question below, letters stand for numbers. Work out the answer to the sum and write its **letter** in the brackets or mark the appropriate box on the multiple choice answer sheet.

A = 8, B = 10, C = 3, D = 2, E = 6,

C x D x C - B = (____)

Question 5

A B C D E F G H I J K L M N O P Q R S T U V W X Y Z

In this question a word had been written in code. An example has been worked out for you. You must now work out the missing code in the same way. Write the code in the space provided or mark the appropriate box on the multiple choice answer sheet.

If the code for **CREAM** is **AVCEK**,

what is the code for **SWEET**?

_____

Question 6

In the question below, the three words in the second group should go together in the same way as the three in the first group. Find the missing word from the second group and write it in the space provide or mark the appropriate box on the multiple choice answer sheet.

blame   [table]   fault

undid [_____]   voter

Question 7

In this question you need to find the number that should appear in the brackets and completes the sum correctly. Write this number in the space provided or mark the appropriate box on the multiple choice answer sheet.

4 x 7 + 18 = 6 x 6 + (_____)

Question 8

In this question the numbers in each group are related in the same way. You must find the missing number in the third group and write it in the space provided or mark the appropriate box on the multiple choice answer sheet.

(7 [84] 6)   (5 [90] 9)

(6 [____] 8)

Question 9

In the sentence below, one word, which is in capitals, has had **three consecutive** letters taken out. These **three** letters will make one correctly spelt word without changing their order. Write the **three-letter** word in the space provided or mark the appropriate box on the multiple choice answer sheet.

Mary read the **PASE** to the whole class.

Answer _____

Question 10

Below you will see four words and three of their codes. One of the codes is missing. Using the same code, convert the word or number below. Write the answer in the brackets or mark the appropriate box on the multiple choice answer sheet.

TAPE   BEAT   REST   STAB
5281   2893   6352

Find the word for the code **23865** (_____)

© IPS Educational Publishing 2004

Daily Test 9

Question 1

In the question below, the three words in the second group should go together in the same way as the three in the first group. Find the missing word from the second group and write it in the space provide or mark the appropriate box on the multiple choice answer sheet.

flint   [sniff]   fleas

spurn [_____] treat

Question 2

In this question you need to find the number that should appear in the brackets and completes the sum correctly. Write this number in the space provided or mark the appropriate box on the multiple choice answer sheet.

$39 \div 3 \times 2 = 36 + 17 - ($ _____ $)$

Question 3

In this question the numbers in each group are related in the same way. You must find the missing number in the third group and write it in the space provided or mark the appropriate box on the multiple choice answer sheet.

(15 [50] 10)   (20 [56] 8)

(19 [____] 11)

Question 4

In the sentence below, one word, which is in capitals, has had **three consecutive** letters taken out. These **three** letters will make one correctly spelt word without changing their order. Write the **three-letter** word in the space provided or mark the appropriate box on the multiple choice answer sheet.

The old man's face was very WRLED.

(_____)

Question 5

Below you will see four words and three of their codes. One of the codes is missing. Using the same code, convert the word or number below. Write the answer in the brackets or mark the appropriate box on the multiple choice answer sheet.

CORN   RACE   BASE   BEAD

9253   1847   9326

Find the code for the word **BROAD** (_____)

Question 6

In the question below, **one** letter from the word on the left must be moved into the word on the right to make **two** new words. The letters must not be re-arranged. **Both** new words must make sense.
Write the correct letter in the space provided or mark the appropriate box on the multiple choice answer sheet.

THANK   CLOT   Answer ………...

Question 7

In this question you must find two words, **one** from each group, that are the **closest in meaning**.
Underline each of these two words or mark the appropriate boxes on the multiple choice answer sheet

(leap   skip   jump)

(hit   miss   flight)

Question 8

In this question find the **two** words, **one** from each group that will complete the sentence in the best way. **Underline** one word from each group or mark the appropriate boxes on the multiple choice answer sheet.

Artist is to (painter, brush, painting)

as author is to (write, book, fiction).

Question 9

In each question below, letters stand for numbers. Work out the answer to the sum and write its **letter** in the brackets or mark the appropriate box on the multiple choice answer sheet.

A = 75, B = 4, C = 50, D = 25, E = 100,

B x C - E - A = (____)

Question 10

A B C D E F G H I J K L M N O P Q R S T U V W X Y Z

In this question a word had been written in code. An example has been worked out for you. You must now work out the missing word using the same code. Write the word in the space provided or mark the appropriate box on the multiple choice answer sheet.

If the code for **CHANCE** is **EKCQEH**

what does **UTWDTH** mean? _____

Daily Test 10

Question 1

In the question below, find one letter that will complete the word in front of the brackets and begin the word after the brackets.
The same letter must fit into both sets of brackets.
Write the letter on the answer sheet or mark the appropriate box on the multiple choice answer sheet.

CAL (___) ICE   :   WHIR (___) INE

Question 2

In this question you need to find the number that should appear in the brackets and will continue the series in the most sensible way. Write this number in the space provided or mark the appropriate box on the multiple choice answer sheet.

7,   14,   17,   34,   37,   74`,   (____)

Question 3

In the sentence below, a word of four letters is hidden at the end of one word and the beginning of the next word.
Underline the **pair** of words that contain the hidden word or mark the appropriate box on the multiple choice answer sheet.

Father also loaned me fifteen pounds.

Question 4

A B C D E F G H I J K L M N O P Q R S T U V W X Y Z

In the question below, find the pair of letters that will complete the sentence in the best way and write the correct answer in the answer box or mark the appropriate box on the multiple choice answer sheet.

PT is to **SV**
as **TP** is to (_____)

Question 5

In the question below, there are two pairs of words. You must find the word from the list that will go equally well with both pairs of words in the brackets.
Underline this word or mark the appropriate box on the multiple choice answer sheet.

LANE   SHADOW   ROAD   TRACK   PURSUE

(PATH   TRAIL)   (HUNT   FOLLOW)

Question 6

In this question there are three pairs of words. You must complete the third pair in the same way as the first two pairs. Write the correct letter in the space provided or mark the appropriate box on the multiple choice answer sheet.

(bottom, tomb)   (damage, aged)

(master, _____)

Question 7

In the question below, find two words, **one** from each group, that are the **most opposite in meaning**.
Underline each of these two words or mark the appropriate boxes on the multiple choice answer sheet

(weight   often   partly)

(seldom   frequent   length)

Question 8

In the question below, find the **two** words that are **different** from the other three and **underline** them on the answer sheet or mark the appropriate box on the multiple choice answer sheet.

station   port   siding   harbour   bay

Question 9

A B C D E F G H I J K L M N O P Q R S T U V W X Y Z

In this question you need to find the pair of letters that will complete the sequence in the best way and write the correct answer in the answer box or mark the appropriate box on the multiple choice answer sheet.

MJ,   NH,   PF,   SD,   WB,   (_____)

Question 10

In the question below, choose **two** words, **one** from each set, that will together make **one** correctly spelt word. You may not change the order of the letters.
The word from the set on the top always comes first.
Underline the two words or mark the appropriate boxes on the multiple choice answer sheet.

(gear   gall   tall)

(on   in   an)

Daily Test 11

Score. _____

Question 1

In the question below, the three words in the second group should go together in the same way as the three in the first group. Find the missing word from the second group and write it in the space provide or mark the appropriate box on the multiple choice answer sheet.

dance   [mince]   chime

month [_____] chart

Question 2

In this question you need to find the number that should appear in the brackets and completes the sum correctly. Write this number in the space provided or mark the appropriate box on the multiple choice answer sheet.

16 x 3 + 12 = 10 x 3 x (_____)

Question 3

In this question the numbers in each group are related in the same way. You must find the missing number in the third group and write it in the space provided or mark the appropriate box on the multiple choice answer sheet.

(27 [65] 35)   (34 [75] 38)

(40 [____] 38)

Question 4

In the sentence below, one word, which is in capitals, has had **three consecutive** letters taken out. These **three** letters will make one correctly spelt word without changing their order. Write the **three-letter** word in the space provided or mark the appropriate box on the multiple choice answer sheet.

We watched the skater **GE** over the ice..

Answer _____

Question 5

Below you will see four words and three of their codes. One of the codes is missing. Using the same code, convert the word or number below. Write the answer in the brackets or mark the appropriate box on the multiple choice answer sheet.

LINE   MALE   NAIL   OMIT
6728   3471   2576

Find the code for the word **MOTION** (_____)

Question 6

In the question below, **one** letter from the word on the left must be moved into the word on the right to make **two** new words. The letters must not be re-arranged.
Both new words must make sense.
Write the correct letter in the space provided or mark the appropriate box on the multiple choice answer sheet.

PLEAD   READ   (_____)

Question 7

In this question you must find two words, **one** from each group, that are the **closest in meaning**.
Underline each of these two words or mark the appropriate boxes on the multiple choice answer sheet

(spite   site   slight)

(location   locality   ignore)

Question 8

In this question find the two words, one from each group that will complete the sentence in the best way. **Underline** one word from each group or mark the appropriate boxes on the multiple choice answer sheet.

Chemistry is to (laboratory, chemicals, science)

as Spanish is to (bulls, language, holiday).

Question 9

In each question below, letters stand for numbers. Work out the answer to the sum and write its **letter** in the brackets or mark the appropriate box on the multiple choice answer sheet.

A = 27,   B = 9,   C = 18,   D = 3,   E = 6,

C ÷ E x B - B = (____)

Question 10

A B C D E F G H I J K L M N O P Q R S T U V W X Y Z

In this question a word had been written in code. An example has been worked out for you. You must now work out the missing word using the same code. Write the word in the space provided or mark the appropriate box on the multiple choice answer sheet.

If the code for **BRIGHT** is DTKIJV,

what does **EQNQWT** mean? _____

© IPS Educational Publishing 2004

Daily Test 12

Score. _____

Question 1

In the question below, find one letter that will complete the word in front of the brackets and begin the word after the brackets.
The same letter must fit into both sets of brackets.
Write the letter on the answer sheet or mark the appropriate box on the multiple choice answer sheet.

LEA (___) INE : YAR (___) IGHT

Question 2

In this question you need to find the number that should appear in the brackets and will continue the series in the most sensible way. Write this number in the space provided or mark the appropriate box on the multiple choice answer sheet.

5, 6, 8, 8, 9, 11, 11, (____)

Question 3

In the sentence below, a word of four letters is hidden at the end of one word and the beginning of the next word.
Underline the **pair** of words that contain the hidden word or mark the appropriate box on the multiple choice answer sheet.

Special songs are sung at Christmas.

Question 4

A B C D E F G H I J K L M N O P Q R S T U V W X Y Z

In the question below, find the pair of letters that will complete the sentence in the best way and write the correct answer in the answer box or mark the appropriate box on the multiple choice answer sheet.

JP is to **NM**

as **GF** is to (_____)

Question 5

In the question below, there are two pairs of words. You must find the word from the list that will go equally well with both pairs of words in the brackets.
Underline this word or mark the appropriate box on the multiple choice answer sheet.

ESCAPE   DESERT   OASIS   FLY   LEAVES

(SAND   WILDERNESS)   (FLEE   ABANDON)

Question 6

In this question there are three pairs of words. You must complete the third pair in the same way as the first two pairs. Write the correct letter in the space provided or mark the appropriate box on the multiple choice answer sheet.

(deface, cafe)   (strife, fire)

(insert, _____)

Question 7

In the question below, find two words, **one** from each group, that are the **most opposite in meaning**.
Underline each of these two words or mark the appropriate boxes on the multiple choice answer sheet

(force   break   steam)

(accelerate   repair   power)

Question 8

In the question below, find the **two** words that are **different** from the other three and **underline** them on the answer sheet or mark the appropriate box on the multiple choice answer sheet.

motorway   services   pavement   highway   road

Question 9

A B C D E F G H I J K L M N O P Q R S T U V W X Y Z

In this question you need to find the pair of letters that will complete the sequence in the best way and write the correct answer in the answer box or mark the appropriate box on the multiple choice answer sheet.

PD, MB, KY, HW, FT, (_____)

Question 10

In the question below, choose **two** words, **one** from each set, that will together make **one** correctly spelt word. You may not change the order of the letters.
The word from the set on the top always comes first.
Underline the two words or mark the appropriate boxes on the multiple choice answer sheet.

(ball   bat   club)

(end   on   tell)

Daily Test 13

Question 1

In this question there are three pairs of words. You must complete the third pair in the same way as the first two pairs. Write the correct letter in the space provided or mark the appropriate box on the multiple choice answer sheet.

(dart, cart)   (mast, last)

(mace, _____)

Question 2

In the question below, find two words, **one** from each group, that are the **most opposite in meaning**.

Underline each of these two words or mark the appropriate boxes on the multiple choice answer sheet

(lean   keen   mean)

(obvious   anxious   generous)

Question 3

In the question below, find the **two** words that are **different** from the other three and **underline** them on the answer sheet or mark the appropriate box on the multiple choice answer sheet.

thin   lenient   merciful   slender   compassionate

Question 4

A B C D E F G H I J K L M N O P Q R S T U V W X Y Z

In this question you need to find the pair of letters that will complete the sequence in the best way and write the correct answer in the answer box or mark the appropriate box on the multiple choice answer sheet.

CH,   AJ,   YL,   WN,   UP,   (_____)

Question 5

In the question below, choose **two** words, **one** from each set, that will together make **one** correctly spelt word. You may not change the order of the letters.
The word from the set on the top always comes first.
Underline the two words or mark the appropriate boxes on the multiple choice answer sheet.

(bet   bin   ban)

(went   in   go)

Question 6

In the question below, find one letter that will complete the word in front of the brackets and begin the word after the brackets.
The same letter must fit into both sets of brackets.
Write the letter between the brackets on the sheet or mark the appropriate box on the multiple choice answer sheet.

SUC (___) ERB   :   MUC (___) OLE

Question 7

In this question you need to find the number that should appear in the brackets and will continue the series in the most sensible way. Write this number in the space provided or mark the appropriate box on the multiple choice answer sheet.

80,   40,   36,   18,   14,   (____)

Question 8

In the sentence below, a word of four letters is hidden at the end of one word and the beginning of the next word. **Underline** the **pair** of words that contain the hidden word or mark the appropriate box on the multiple choice answer sheet.

They must win their match today.

Question 9

A B C D E F G H I J K L M N O P Q R S T U V W X Y Z

In the question below, find the pair of letters that will complete the sentence in the best way and write the correct answer in the answer box or mark the appropriate box on the multiple choice answer sheet.

FJ is to DG

as HM is to (_____)

Question 10

In the question below, there are two pairs of words. You must find the word from the list that will go equally well with both pairs of words in the brackets.
Underline this word or mark the appropriate box on the multiple choice answer sheet.

BRIGHT   COUNT   SMART   BRAINY   SNAPPY

(INTELLIGENT   CLEVER) (NEAT   TIDY)

Daily Test 14

Question 1

In the question below, **one** letter from the word on the left must be moved into the word on the right to make **two** new words. The letters must not be re-arranged.
Both new words must make sense.
Write the correct letter in the space provided or mark the appropriate box on the multiple choice answer sheet.

GROWN   FAME   (_____)

Question 2

In this question you must find two words, **one** from each group, that are the **closest in meaning**.
Underline each of these two words or mark the appropriate boxes on the multiple choice answer sheet

(taunt   test   haunt)

(chase   tease   charge)

Question 3

In this question find the **two** words, <u>one</u> from each group that will complete the sentence in the best way.
Underline one word from each group or mark the appropriate boxes on the multiple choice answer sheet.

Chicken is to (egg, wing, chick)

as cow is to (beef, calf, bull).

Question 4

In each question below, letters stand for numbers. Work out the answer to the sum and write its **letter** in the brackets or mark the appropriate box on the multiple choice answer sheet.

A = 8, B = 16, C = 12, D = 4, E = 6,

B ÷ D x D - A = (____)

Question 5

A B C D E F G H I J K L M N O P Q R S T U V W X Y Z

In this question a word had been written in code. An example has been worked out for you. You must now work out the missing code in the same way. Write the code in the space provided or mark the appropriate box on the multiple choice answer sheet.

If the code for **FUTURE** is **BRPRNB**,

what is the code for **ALIENS**?

_____

Question 6

In the question below, the three words in the second group should go together in the same way as the three in the first group. Find the missing word from the second group and write it in the space provide or mark the appropriate box on the multiple choice answer sheet.

table   [steal]   blast

rifle [_____] smack

Question 7

In this question you need to find the number that should appear in the brackets and completes the sum correctly. Write this number in the space provided or mark the appropriate box on the multiple choice answer sheet.

180 - 27 - 53 = 8 x 9 + (_____)

Question 8

In this question the numbers in each group are related in the same way. You must find the missing number in the third group and write it in the space provided or mark the appropriate box on the multiple choice answer sheet.

(20 [78] 48)   (25 [88] 53)

(24 [____] 36)

Question 9

In the sentence below, one word, which is in capitals, has had **three consecutive** letters taken out. These **three** letters will make one correctly spelt word without changing their order. Write the **three-letter** word in the space provided or mark the appropriate box on the multiple choice answer sheet.

My sister **ATDS** the local dancing school.

Answer _____

Question 10

Below you will see four words and three of their codes. One of the codes is missing. Using the same code, convert the word or number below. Write the answer in the brackets or mark the appropriate box on the multiple choice answer sheet.

CHAT   HEAR   REST   RACE
7345   5463   6742

Find the word for the code **6745235** (_____)

Daily Test 15

Score. _____

Question 1

In the question below, find one letter that will complete the word in front of the brackets and begin the word after the brackets.
The same letter must fit into both sets of brackets.
Write the letter on the answer sheet or mark the appropriate box on the multiple choice answer sheet.

CLEA (___) AKE　　:　　BOA (___) OCK

Question 2

In this question you need to find the number that should appear in the brackets and will continue the series in the most sensible way. Write this number in the space provided or mark the appropriate box on the multiple choice answer sheet.

169,　121,　81,　49,　25,　(____)

Question 3

In the sentence below, a word of four letters is hidden at the end of one word and the beginning of the next word.
Underline the **pair** of words that contain the hidden word or mark the appropriate box on the multiple choice answer sheet.

They got themselves into trouble yesterday.

Question 4

A B C D E F G H I J K L M N O P Q R S T U V W X Y Z

In the question below, find the pair of letters that will complete the sentence in the best way and write the correct answer in the answer box or mark the appropriate box on the multiple choice answer sheet.

PL　is to　MM

as　UR　is to　(_____)

Question 5

In the question below, there are two pairs of words. You must find the word from the list that will go equally well with both pairs of words in the brackets.
Underline this word or mark the appropriate box on the multiple choice answer sheet.

CHEAT　PUNCH　BETRAY　PUPPET　FOOL

(DECEIVE　MISLEAD)　(CLOWN　JESTER)

Question 6

In this question there are three pairs of words. You must complete the third pair in the same way as the first two pairs. Write the correct letter in the space provided or mark the appropriate box on the multiple choice answer sheet.

(vessel,　less)　　(repeat,　tape)

(scream,　_____)

Question 7

In the question below, find two words, **one** from each group, that are the **most opposite in meaning**.
Underline each of these two words or mark the appropriate boxes on the multiple choice answer sheet

(ready　steady　cook)

(unprepared　steadfast　steaming)

Question 8

In the question below, find the **two** words that are **different** from the other three and **underline** them on the answer sheet or mark the appropriate box on the multiple choice answer sheet.

square　　cube　　octahedron　　tetrahedron　　rectangle

Question 9

A B C D E F G H I J K L M N O P Q R S T U V W X Y Z

In this question you need to find the pair of letters that will complete the sequence in the best way and write the correct answer in the answer box or mark the appropriate box on the multiple choice answer sheet.

MQ,　NP,　PN,　QM,　SK,　(_____)

Question 10

In the question below, choose **two** words, **one** from each set, that will together make **one** correctly spelt word. You may not change the order of the letters.
The word from the set on the top always comes first.
Underline the two words or mark the appropriate boxes on the multiple choice answer sheet.

(not　net　ten)

(work　play　wink)

Daily Test 16

Question 1

In the question below, **one** letter from the word on the left must be moved into the word on the right to make **two** new words. The letters must not be re-arranged.
Both new words must make sense.
Write the correct letter in the space provided or mark the appropriate box on the multiple choice answer sheet.

PLEAD   PIER   (_____)

Question 2

In this question you must find two words, **one** from each group, that are the **closest in meaning**.
Underline each of these two words or mark the appropriate boxes on the multiple choice answer sheet

(action   active   actor)

(lively   expensive   acute)

Question 3

In this question find the two words, one from each group that will complete the sentence in the best way.
Underline one word from each group or mark the appropriate boxes on the multiple choice answer sheet.

Soldier is to (gun, uniform, army)

as sailor is to (sea, ship, navy).

Question 4

In each question below, letters stand for numbers. Work out the answer to the sum and write its **letter** in the brackets or mark the appropriate box on the multiple choice answer sheet.

A = 24, B = 3, C = 8, D = 2, E = 12,

A ÷ B - C + A = (_____)

Question 5

A B C D E F G H I J K L M N O P Q R S T U V W X Y Z

In this question a word had been written in code. An example has been worked out for you. You must now work out the missing code in the same way. Write the code in the space provided or mark the appropriate box on the multiple choice answer sheet.

If the code for **BRANCH** is **CPBLDF**,

what is the code for **TRUNKS**? (_____)

Question 6

In the question below, the three words in the second group should go together in the same way as the three in the first group. Find the missing word from the second group and write it in the space provide or mark the appropriate box on the multiple choice answer sheet.

slant   [tales]   steal

spear [_____] yolks

Question 7

In this question you need to find the number that should appear in the brackets and completes the sum correctly. Write this number in the space provided or mark the appropriate box on the multiple choice answer sheet.

64 ÷ 8 x 3 = 63 - 15 - (_____)

Question 8

In this question the numbers in each group are related in the same way. You must find the missing number in the third group and write it in the space provided or mark the appropriate box on the multiple choice answer sheet.

(35 [60] 10)   (40 [60] 20)

(50 [____] 30)

Question 9

In the sentence below, one word, which is in capitals, has had **three consecutive** letters taken out. These **three** letters will make one correctly spelt word without changing their order. Write the **three-letter** word in the space provided or mark the appropriate box on the multiple choice answer sheet.

We paddled our **OES** along the river.

Answer _____

Question 10

Below you will see four words and three of their codes. One of the codes is missing. Using the same code, convert the word or number below. Write the answer in the brackets or mark the appropriate box on the multiple choice answer sheet.

LEAN   BAND   BELT   DENT
1347   5397   9324

Find the word for the code **72593** (_____)

Daily Test 17

Question 1

In the question below, the three words in the second group should go together in the same way as the three in the first group. Find the missing word from the second group and write it in the space provide or mark the appropriate box on the multiple choice answer sheet.

cheat   [dance]   handy

treat [_____] gasps

Question 2

In this question you need to find the number that should appear in the brackets and completes the sum correctly. Write this number in the space provided or mark the appropriate box on the multiple choice answer sheet.

$$44 + 27 + 36 = 24 \times 3 + (\text{\_\_\_\_})$$

Question 3

In this question the numbers in each group are related in the same way. You must find the missing number in the third group and write it in the space provided or mark the appropriate box on the multiple choice answer sheet.

(67 [42] 30)   (81 [49] 37)

(47 [___] 28)

Question 4

In the sentence below, one word, which is in capitals, has had **three consecutive** letters taken out. These **three** letters will make one correctly spelt word without changing their order. Write the **three-letter** word in the space provided or mark the appropriate box on the multiple choice answer sheet.

The floor was made from thick **CET**.

(_____)

Question 5

Below you will see four words and three of their codes. One of the codes is missing. Using the same code, convert the word or number below. Write the answer in the brackets or mark the appropriate box on the multiple choice answer sheet.

STAY   DUST   TABS   BEDS

7186   6945   8269

Find the code for the word **BEAST** (_____)

Question 6

In the question below, **one** letter from the word on the left must be moved into the word on the right to make **two** new words. The letters must not be re-arranged. **Both** new words must make sense. Write the correct letter in the space provided or mark the appropriate box on the multiple choice answer sheet.

STABLE   OWLS   (_____)

Question 7

In this question you must find two words, **one** from each group, that are the **closest in meaning**. **Underline** each of these two words or mark the appropriate boxes on the multiple choice answer sheet

(rare   rarest   fairest)

(inform   infrequent   income)

Question 8

In this question find the two words, one from each group that will complete the sentence in the best way. **Underline** one word from each group or mark the appropriate boxes on the multiple choice answer sheet.

water is to (pond, pipe, wine)

as electricity is to (wire, light, spark).

Question 9

In each question below, letters stand for numbers. Work out the answer to the sum and write its **letter** in the brackets or mark the appropriate box on the multiple choice answer sheet.

A = 7, B = 11, C = 8, D = 12, E = 3,

A x E - B - A = (___)

Question 10

A B C D E F G H I J K L M N O P Q R S T U V W X Y Z

In this question a word had been written in code. An example has been worked out for you. You must now work out the missing word using the same code. Write the word in the space provided or mark the appropriate box on the multiple choice answer sheet.

If the code for **BRIGHT** is **CTJIIV**

what does **EKTOBN** mean? _____

Daily Test 18

Question 1

In the question below, find one letter that will complete the word in front of the brackets and begin the word after the brackets.
The same letter must fit into both sets of brackets.
Write the letter on the answer sheet or mark the appropriate box on the multiple choice answer sheet.

RAT (___) PINE　　:　　FOCU (___) EAL

Question 2

In this question you need to find the number that should appear in the brackets and will continue the series in the most sensible way.　Write this number in the space provided or mark the appropriate box on the multiple choice answer sheet.

21,　28,　24,　32,　27,　36,　30,　(____)

Question 3

In the sentence below, a word of four letters is hidden at the end of one word and the beginning of the next word. **Underline** the **pair** of words that contain the hidden word or mark the appropriate box on the multiple choice answer sheet.

Some exciting things might occur later.

Question 4

A B C D E F G H I J K L M N O P Q R S T U V W X Y Z

In the question below, find the pair of letters that will complete the sentence in the best way and write the correct answer in the answer box or mark the appropriate box on the multiple choice answer sheet.

GW is to **FX**

as **TP** is to (____)

Question 5

In the question below, there are two pairs of words. You must find the word from the list that will go equally well with both pairs of words in the brackets.
Underline this word or mark the appropriate box on the multiple choice answer sheet.

BOUNCE　BANK　HURDLE　VAULT　SECURE

(JUMP　LEAP)　(SAFE　STRONGROOM)

Question 6

In this question there are three pairs of words. You must complete the third pair in the same way as the first two pairs. Write the correct letter in the space provided or mark the appropriate box on the multiple choice answer sheet.

(parade, dare)　(minute, tune)

(divide, _____)

Question 7

In the question below, find two words, **one** from each group, that are the **most opposite in meaning**.
Underline each of these two words or mark the appropriate boxes on the multiple choice answer sheet

(foreign　forfeit　forbidden)

(permit　permissible　permission)

Question 8

In the question below, find the **two** words that are **different** from the other three and **underline** them on the answer sheet or mark the appropriate box on the multiple choice answer sheet.

dash　line　drop　race　hurry

Question 9

A B C D E F G H I J K L M N O P Q R S T U V W X Y Z

In this question you need to find the pair of letters that will complete the sequence in the best way and write the correct answer in the answer box or mark the appropriate box on the multiple choice answer sheet.

ZD,　WH,　TL,　QP,　NT,　(____)

Question 10

In the question below, choose **two** words, **one** from each set, that will together make **one** correctly spelt word. You may not change the order of the letters.
The word from the set on the top always comes first.
Underline the two words or mark the appropriate boxes on the multiple choice answer sheet.

(post　stamp　letter)

(card　album　stake)

Daily Test 19

Question 1

In the question below, the three words in the second group should go together in the same way as the three in the first group. Find the missing word from the second group and write it in the space provide or mark the appropriate box on the multiple choice answer sheet.

break   [baker]   cakes

crest [_____] eager

Question 2

In this question you need to find the number that should appear in the brackets and completes the sum correctly. Write this number in the space provided or mark the appropriate box on the multiple choice answer sheet.

47 + 25 - 8 = 8 x 6 + (_____)

Question 3

In this question the numbers in each group are related in the same way. You must find the missing number in the third group and write it in the space provided or mark the appropriate box on the multiple choice answer sheet.

(42 [14] 6)   (25 [10] 5)

(36 [____] 6)

Question 4

In the sentence below, one word, which is in capitals, has had **three consecutive** letters taken out. These **three** letters will make one correctly spelt word without changing their order. Write the **three-letter** word in the space provided or mark the appropriate box on the multiple choice answer sheet.

In America they drive on the **HT**.

Answer _____

Question 5

Below you will see four words and three of their codes. One of the codes is missing. Using the same code, convert the word or number below. Write the answer in the brackets or mark the appropriate box on the multiple choice answer sheet.

DIRE   MAID   RACE   CRAM
6259   9581   2567

Find the code for the word **DREAM** (_____)

Question 6

In the question below, **one** letter from the word on the left must be moved into the word on the right to make **two** new words. The letters must not be re-arranged. **Both** new words must make sense. Write the correct letter in the space provided or mark the appropriate box on the multiple choice answer sheet.

PAINT   SILTS   (_____)

Question 7

In this question you must find two words, **one** from each group, that are the **closest in meaning**. **Underline** each of these two words or mark the appropriate boxes on the multiple choice answer sheet

(connect   donate   donor)

(present   give   receive)

Question 8

In this question find the two words, one from each group that will complete the sentence in the best way. **Underline** one word from each group or mark the appropriate boxes on the multiple choice answer sheet.

Tale is to (story, tail, stale)

as roll is to (stroll, part, role).

Question 9

In each question below, letters stand for numbers. Work out the answer to the sum and write its **letter** in the brackets or mark the appropriate box on the multiple choice answer sheet.

A = 16, B = 4, C = 3, D = 12, E = 8,

E x C - A - B = (____)

Question 10

A B C D E F G H I J K L M N O P Q R S T U V W X Y Z

In this question a word had been written in code. An example has been worked out for you. You must now work out the missing word using the same code. Write the word in the space provided or mark the appropriate box on the multiple choice answer sheet.

If the code for **SIMPLE** is **PLJSIH**,

what does **ADKFBU** mean? _____

Daily Test 20

Score. _____

Question 1

In the question below, find one letter that will complete the word in front of the brackets and begin the word after the brackets.
The same letter must fit into both sets of brackets.
Write the letter on the answer sheet or mark the appropriate box on the multiple choice answer sheet.

SOR (___) RIP　　:　　STAR (___) ENT

Question 2

In this question you need to find the number that should appear in the brackets and will continue the series in the most sensible way. Write this number in the space provided or mark the appropriate box on the multiple choice answer sheet.

360,　72,　18,　6,　(____)

Question 3

In the sentence below, a word of four letters is hidden at the end of one word and the beginning of the next word.
Underline the **pair** of words that contain the hidden word or mark the appropriate box on the multiple choice answer sheet.

The switch operated the large television.

Question 4

A B C D E F G H I J K L M N O P Q R S T U V W X Y Z

In the question below, find the pair of letters that will complete the sentence in the best way and write the correct answer in the answer box or mark the appropriate box on the multiple choice answer sheet.

DL is to **AN**

as **EH** is to　(_____)

Question 5

In the question below, there are two pairs of words. You must find the word from the list that will go equally well with both pairs of words in the brackets.
Underline this word or mark the appropriate box on the multiple choice answer sheet.

DECAYED　CHEESY　DEVIL　BAD　TERRIBLE

(ROTTEN　MOULDY)　(EVIL　WICKED)

Question 6

In this question there are three pairs of words. You must complete the third pair in the same way as the first two pairs. Write the correct letter in the space provided or mark the appropriate box on the multiple choice answer sheet.

(decode, coded)　(strand, rants)

(master, _____)

Question 7

In the question below, find two words, **one** from each group, that are the **most opposite in meaning**.
Underline each of these two words or mark the appropriate boxes on the multiple choice answer sheet

(tired　relaxed　tight)

(slack　stick　stack)

Question 8

In the question below, find the **two** words that are **different** from the other three and **underline** them on the answer sheet or mark the appropriate box on the multiple choice answer sheet.

depart　exit　door　passage　leave

Question 9

A B C D E F G H I J K L M N O P Q R S T U V W X Y Z

In this question you need to find the pair of letters that will complete the sequence in the best way and write the correct answer in the answer box or mark the appropriate box on the multiple choice answer sheet.

YC,　BZ,　EW,　HT,　KQ,　(_____)

Question 10

In the question below, choose **two** words, **one** from each set, that will together make **one** correctly spelt word. You may not change the order of the letters.
The word from the set on the top always comes first.
Underline the two words or mark the appropriate boxes on the multiple choice answer sheet.

(by　my　try)

(self　plain　plane)

Multiple choice answer sheet.   Tests 1 to 4.

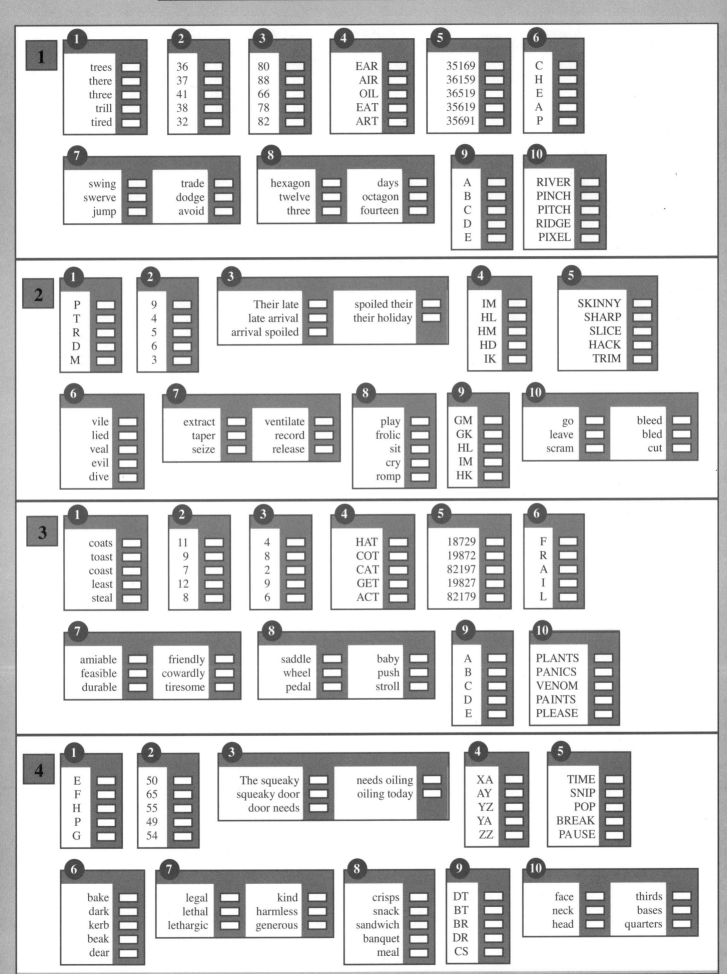

1

1
trees
there
three
trill
tired

2
36
37
41
38
32

3
80
88
66
78
82

4
EAR
AIR
OIL
EAT
ART

5
35169
36159
36519
35619
35691

6
C
H
E
A
P

7
swing
swerve
jump

trade
dodge
avoid

8
hexagon
twelve
three

days
octagon
fourteen

9
A
B
C
D
E

10
RIVER
PINCH
PITCH
RIDGE
PIXEL

2

1
P
T
R
D
M

2
9
4
5
6
3

3
Their late
late arrival
arrival spoiled

spoiled their
their holiday

4
IM
HL
HM
HD
IK

5
SKINNY
SHARP
SLICE
HACK
TRIM

6
vile
lied
veal
evil
dive

7
extract
taper
seize

ventilate
record
release

8
play
frolic
sit
cry
romp

9
GM
GK
HL
IM
HK

10
go
leave
scram

bleed
bled
cut

3

1
coats
toast
coast
least
steal

2
11
9
7
12
8

3
4
8
2
9
6

4
HAT
COT
CAT
GET
ACT

5
18729
19872
82197
19827
82179

6
F
R
A
I
L

7
amiable
feasible
durable

friendly
cowardly
tiresome

8
saddle
wheel
pedal

baby
push
stroll

9
A
B
C
D
E

10
PLANTS
PANICS
VENOM
PAINTS
PLEASE

4

1
E
F
H
P
G

2
50
65
55
49
54

3
The squeaky
squeaky door
door needs

needs oiling
oiling today

4
XA
AY
YZ
YA
ZZ

5
TIME
SNIP
POP
BREAK
PAUSE

6
bake
dark
kerb
beak
dear

7
legal
lethal
lethargic

kind
harmless
generous

8
crisps
snack
sandwich
banquet
meal

9
DT
BT
BR
DR
CS

10
face
neck
head

thirds
bases
quarters

Multiple choice answer sheet.   Tests 5 to 8.

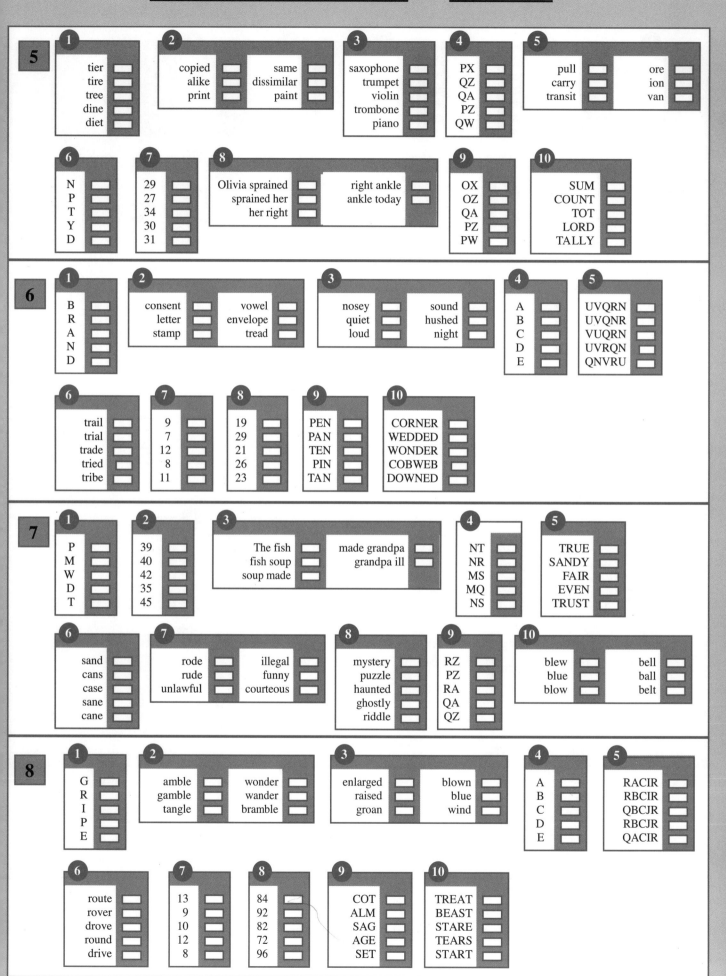

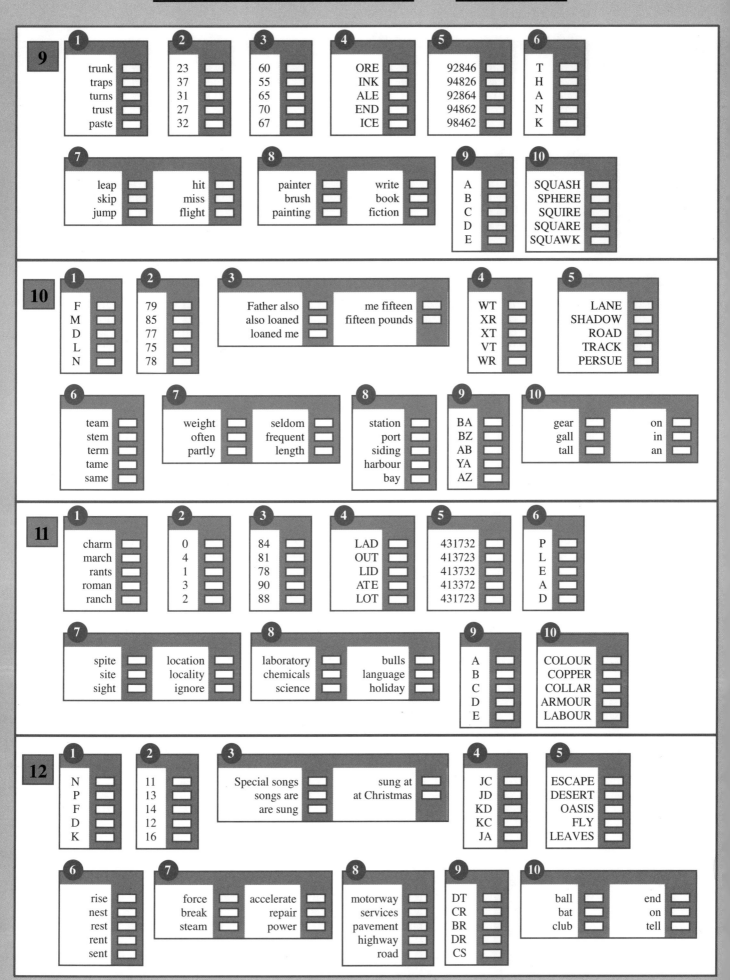

9

1
trunk
traps
turns
trust
paste

2
23
37
31
27
32

3
60
55
65
70
67

4
ORE
INK
ALE
END
ICE

5
92846
94826
92864
94862
98462

6
T
H
A
N
K

7
leap
skip
jump

hit
miss
flight

8
painter
brush
painting

write
book
fiction

9
A
B
C
D
E

10
SQUASH
SPHERE
SQUIRE
SQUARE
SQUAWK

10

1
F
M
D
L
N

2
79
85
77
75
78

3
Father also
also loaned
loaned me

me fifteen
fifteen pounds

4
WT
XR
XT
VT
WR

5
LANE
SHADOW
ROAD
TRACK
PERSUE

6
team
stem
term
tame
same

7
weight
often
partly

seldom
frequent
length

8
station
port
siding
harbour
bay

9
BA
BZ
AB
YA
AZ

10
gear
gall
tall

on
in
an

11

1
charm
march
rants
roman
ranch

2
0
4
1
3
2

3
84
81
78
90
88

4
LAD
OUT
LID
ATE
LOT

5
431732
413723
413732
413372
431723

6
P
L
E
A
D

7
spite
site
sight

location
locality
ignore

8
laboratory
chemicals
science

bulls
language
holiday

9
A
B
C
D
E

10
COLOUR
COPPER
COLLAR
ARMOUR
LABOUR

12

1
N
P
F
D
K

2
11
13
14
12
16

3
Special songs
songs are
are sung

sung at
at Christmas

4
JC
JD
KD
KC
JA

5
ESCAPE
DESERT
OASIS
FLY
LEAVES

6
rise
nest
rest
rent
sent

7
force
break
steam

accelerate
repair
power

8
motorway
services
pavement
highway
road

9
DT
CR
BR
DR
CS

10
ball
bat
club

end
on
tell

Multiple choice answer sheet.   Tests 13 to 16.

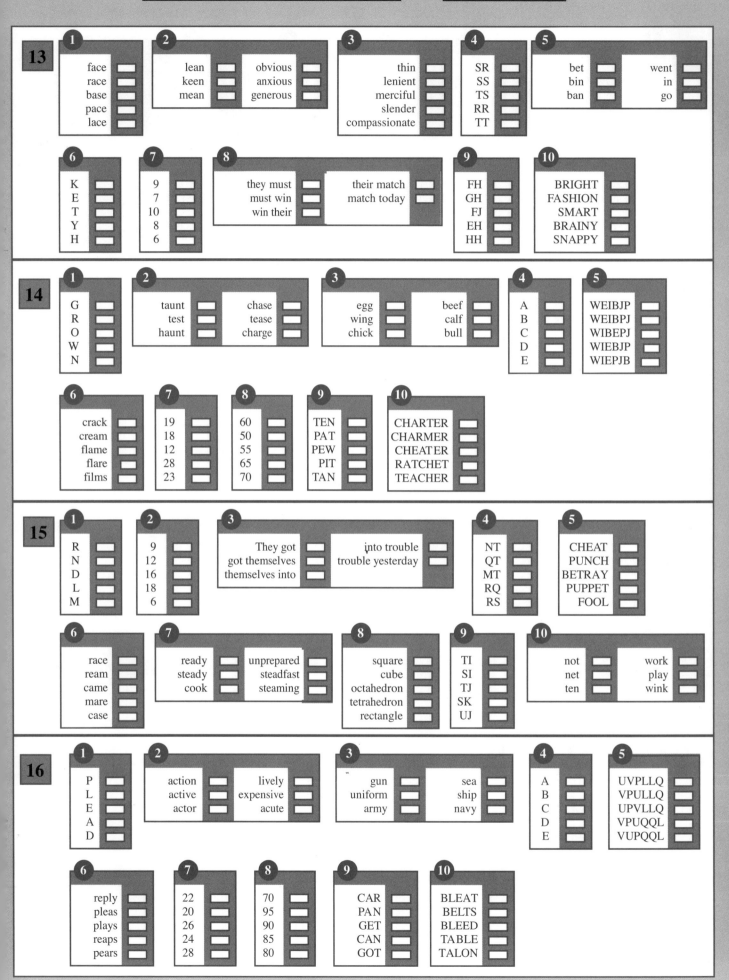

13

1
face
race
base
pace
lace

2
lean
keen
mean
| obvious
anxious
generous

3
thin
lenient
merciful
slender
compassionate

4
SR
SS
TS
RR
TT

5
bet
bin
ban
| went
in
go

6
K
E
T
Y
H

7
9
7
10
8
6

8
they must
must win
win their
| their match
match today

9
FH
GH
FJ
EH
HH

10
BRIGHT
FASHION
SMART
BRAINY
SNAPPY

14

1
G
R
O
W
N

2
taunt
test
haunt
| chase
tease
charge

3
egg
wing
chick
| beef
calf
bull

4
A
B
C
D
E

5
WEIBJP
WEIBPJ
WIBEPJ
WIEBJP
WIEPJB

6
crack
cream
flame
flare
films

7
19
18
12
28
23

8
60
50
55
65
70

9
TEN
PAT
PEW
PIT
TAN

10
CHARTER
CHARMER
CHEATER
RATCHET
TEACHER

15

1
R
N
D
L
M

2
9
12
16
18
6

3
They got
got themselves
themselves into
| into trouble
trouble yesterday

4
NT
QT
MT
RQ
RS

5
CHEAT
PUNCH
BETRAY
PUPPET
FOOL

6
race
ream
came
mare
case

7
ready
steady
cook
| unprepared
steadfast
steaming

8
square
cube
octahedron
tetrahedron
rectangle

9
TI
SI
TJ
SK
UJ

10
not
net
ten
| work
play
wink

16

1
P
L
E
A
D

2
action
active
actor
| lively
expensive
acute

3
gun
uniform
army
| sea
ship
navy

4
A
B
C
D
E

5
UVPLLQ
VPULLQ
UPVLLQ
VPUQQL
VUPQQL

6
reply
pleas
plays
reaps
pears

7
22
20
26
24
28

8
70
95
90
85
80

9
CAR
PAN
GET
CAN
GOT

10
BLEAT
BELTS
BLEED
TABLE
TALON

Multiple choice answer sheet.   Tests 17 to 20.

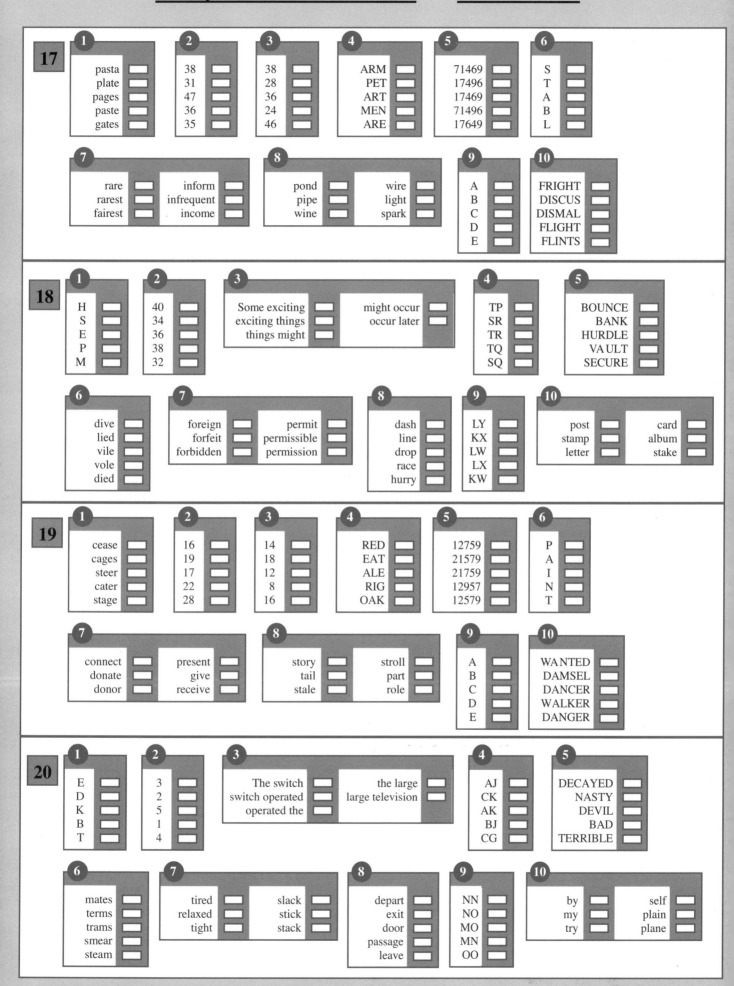

17

1
pasta
plate
pages
paste
gates

2
38
31
47
36
35

3
38
28
36
24
46

4
ARM
PET
ART
MEN
ARE

5
71469
17496
17469
71496
17649

6
S
T
A
B
L

7
rare   inform
rarest   infrequent
fairest   income

8
pond   wire
pipe   light
wine   spark

9
A
B
C
D
E

10
FRIGHT
DISCUS
DISMAL
FLIGHT
FLINTS

18

1
H
S
E
P
M

2
40
34
36
38
32

3
Some exciting   might occur
exciting things   occur later
things might

4
TP
SR
TR
TQ
SQ

5
BOUNCE
BANK
HURDLE
VAULT
SECURE

6
dive
lied
vile
vole
died

7
foreign   permit
forfeit   permissible
forbidden permission

8
dash
line
drop
race
hurry

9
LY
KX
LW
LX
KW

10
post   card
stamp   album
letter   stake

19

1
cease
cages
steer
cater
stage

2
16
19
17
22
28

3
14
18
12
8
16

4
RED
EAT
ALE
RIG
OAK

5
12759
21579
21759
12957
12579

6
P
A
I
N
T

7
connect   present
donate   give
donor   receive

8
story   stroll
tail   part
stale   role

9
A
B
C
D
E

10
WANTED
DAMSEL
DANCER
WALKER
DANGER

20

1
E
D
K
B
T

2
3
2
5
1
4

3
The switch   the large
switch operated   large television
operated the

4
AJ
CK
AK
BJ
CG

5
DECAYED
NASTY
DEVIL
BAD
TERRIBLE

6
mates
terms
trams
smear
steam

7
tired   slack
relaxed stick
tight   stack

8
depart
exit
door
passage
leave

9
NN
NO
MO
MN
OO

10
by   self
my   plain
try   plane

Answers

	Test 1	Test 2	Test 3	Test 4	Test 5
1	there	M	coast	P	tier
2	32	4	9	65	alike / dissimilar
3	78	late arrival (tear)	6	needs oiling (soil)	violin / piano
4	EAR	HL	HAT	ZZ	PZ
5	35619	TRIM	19827	BREAK	transit / ion
6	E	evil	F	KERB	D
7	swerve / dodge	seize / release	amiable / friendly	lethal / harmless	34
8	twelve / fourteen	sit / cry	pedal / push	crisps / sandwich	right ankle (tank)
9	B	HK	E	CS	OZ
10	PITCH	scram / bled	PAINTS	head / quarters	COUNT

	Test 6	Test 7	Test 8	Test 9	Test 10
1	R	W	G	trust	L
2	stamp / tread	45	amble / wander	27	77
3	loud / hushed	grandpa ill (pail)	groan / blue	60	also loaned (solo)
4	B	MS	A	INK	WR
5	UVQNR	FAIR	QACIR	94826	TRACK
6	trial	cans	round	H	term
7	11	rude / courteous	10	skip / miss	often / seldom
8	29	haunted / ghostly	96	painting / book	station / siding
9	TAN	QA	SAG	D	BZ
10	COBWEB	blue / bell	TEARS	SQUARE	gall / on

	Test 11	Test 12	Test 13	Test 14	Test 15
1	ranch	N	lace	R	R
2	2	12	mean / generous	taunt / tease	9
3	81	special songs (also)	thin / slender	chick / calf	trouble / yesterday (eyes)
4	LID	KC	SR	A	RS
5	431732	DESERT	bin / go	WIEBJP	FOOL
6	D	rest	H	cream	mare
7	site / location	break / repair	7	28	ready / unprepared
8	science / language	services / pavement	must win (twin)	70	square / rectangle
9	C	CR	FJ	TEN	TJ
10	COLOUR	bat / on	SMART	CHARTER	net / work

	Test 16	Test 17	Test 18	Test 19	Test 20
1	P	paste	S	cater	T
2	active / lively	35	40	16	3
3	army / navy	24	occur / later (curl)	12	switch operated (chop)
4	A	MEN	SQ	RIG	BJ
5	UPVLLQ	71469	VAULT	12759	BAD
6	reply	B	dive	T	steam
7	24	rare / infrequent	forbidden / permissible	donate / give	tight / slack
8	70	pipe / wire	line / drop	tail / role	door / passage
9	CAN	E	KX	B	NN
10	TABLE	DISMAL	post / card	DANCER	my / self